Valentine Mice!

Valentine Mice!

by Bethany Roberts
Illustrated by Doug Cushman

SCHOLASTIC INC.
New York   Toronto   London   Auckland   Sydney
Mexico City   New Delhi   Hong Kong

ISBN 0-590-96066-0

Text copyright © 1997 by Barbara Beverage.
Illustrations copyright © 1997 by Doug Cushman.
All rights reserved.
Published by Scholastic Inc., 555 Broadway, New York, NY 10012,
by arrangement with Houghton Mifflin Company.

24 23 22   7/0

Printed in the U.S.A.   23

First Scholastic printing, January 1999

Illustrations executed in watercolor. Type is set in 21/24-point Cantoria semi bold.

To my valentines
Bob, Krista and Melissa
—*B. R.*

To my Juney Irene Cushman, my first valentine
—*D. C.*

Valentine mice
deliver valentines—

red, pink.
Skip! Hop!

Up this hill,
then s-l-i-d-e down.

One little mouse
goes *swoosh*! Plop!

One to the rabbit,
two for the squirrels,

10

three for the chipmunks.
Zip! Nip!

11

More to deliver.
Cross the pond.

S-l-i-d-e!   G-l-i-d-e!

Slip!

Flip!

15

Valentines here!

Valentines there!

Shower valentines!

THROW! THROW! THROW!

Valentine mice—
one, two, three . . .

One is missing!
Where can he be?

Valentine mice
look high and low.

Hurry! Worry!
Call! Shout!

Follow these footprints.
Quick! Quick!

There's a mitten!

Pull him out!

All together now . . .

Dig!   Tug!

Push!   P-u-l-l!

YAY!

One little mouse gets a

valentine hug.